an extract from
ali smith's
hotel world
with an enthusiast's view
by kathryn ross

11035537

read around books

an extract from
ali smith's

hotel world

with an enthusiast's view
by kathryn ross

Scottish **Book** Trust

2003

Published by
Scottish Book Trust
Scottish Book Centre
137 Dundee Street
Edinburgh EH11 1BG

Tel: 0131 229 3663

From April 2003 Scottish Book Trust will be moving its offices to Sandeman House, 55 High Street, Edinburgh EH1 1SR.

ISBN: 1 901077 10 1
Copyright © Scottish Book Trust, 2003

All rights reserved. No part of this book may be reproduced, stored in a retrieval system, or transmitted in any form or by any means, electronic, mechanical, photocopying, recording, or otherwise, without the written permission of the publisher.

Published with the support of the Scottish Arts Council National Lottery Fund and The Hugh Fraser Foundation.

Scottish
Arts Council
LOTTERY FUNDED

Hotel World is published by Penguin
ISBN: 0 140 29679 4

Extract copyright © Ali Smith, 2001

Series design by Caleb Rutherford   eidetic
Printed in the UK by Cox & Wyman, Reading, Berkshire

contents

read **around books**

There is no shortage of fiction on the shelves of our bookshops – quite the opposite – but finding one that shouts out 'this is what you are looking for' is getting harder and harder as the number of books published goes up with each passing year. Too often we open a new book with expectation and enthusiasm only to discover disappointment and to struggle to get beyond page thirty. When we do find a book we really enjoy the urge is there to tell friends, colleagues and family to read it too in the hope that they will share our delight.

Read Around Books goes one step further and puts that enthusiasm down in black and white in the hope that many more readers will discover the joys of reading the very finest fiction that has emerged from Scotland over the last one hundred years. **This is a chance to sample before you borrow or buy**. Others have found these books before you, the writing held them spellbound and even when finished, these books would not let their readers go.

Each of the first twelve of these highly collectable little guide books promotes a work of fiction by a writer who lives in Scotland, was born in Scotland or who has been influenced by Scotland (our definition of Scottish is generous). Together they offer a marvellous introduction to the very best of Scottish writing from the twentieth and the first few years of the twenty-first centuries.

In each you will find a substantial extract, the enthusiast's view of the book, starting points for discussion for readers' groups, a short biographical piece about the author, and suggestions for similar reads which act as a further gateway to fine fiction.

Jan Rutherford
Series editor, 2003

the enthusiast

Kathryn Ross

Kathryn Ross has always loved reading and by working as an English teacher, an independent bookseller and latterly as Deputy Director of Scottish Book Trust she has contrived to live her life surrounded by books. In June 2002 she and Lindsey Fraser established Fraser Ross Associates, a literary consultancy representing writers from throughout the UK and offering readership development support to teachers, librarians, parents and carers.

the enthusiast's **view**

Hotel World

by Ali Smith

*H*otel World was shortlisted for both the Orange and the Booker Prize in 2001 and won the Scottish Arts Council Book of the Year Award 2002. It is Ali Smith's second novel.

Wooooooooo-
hooooooo what a fall what a soar what a plummet
what a dash into dark into light what a plunge what a glide
thud crash what a drop what a rush what a swoop what a
fright what a mad hushed skirl what a smash mush mash-
up broke and gashed what a heart in my mouth what an
end.

What a beginning.
Hotel World bursts into exuberant life – with a death. You're caught up and bowled along by the sheer energy and excitement of the opening pages and yet what is being described is almost too awful to contemplate.

With a jubilant whoop, the ghost of Sara Wilby relives her plummet down a lift shaft to oblivion. Not a gentle Alice-in-Wonderland drift to the ground, but an appallingly swift and violent descent. What an end indeed. But of course it's only the beginning.

Set in a branch of a bland, upmarket hotel chain, *Hotel World* offers a glimpse into the lives of five women connected to each other by the tragic death of one of them in a freak accident. On only her second night at the Global, nineteen-year-old Sara Wilby, chambermaid and rising swimming star, bet another hotel employee that she could squeeze herself into the dumb waiter on the top floor. She could, but almost immediately the cords broke and she plunged four storeys to her death.

The five interconnected characters are Sara's ghost; her bereaved sister Clare desperate to know why Sara died; Else Freeman, a homeless woman begging outside the hotel; Penny Warner, journalist and hotel guest; and Lise O'Brien, receptionist at the Global.

So it's about death. But it's also about love, poverty, capitalism, language and metaphysical poetry... just to be going on with. And if that makes *Hotel World* sound like heavy going, it isn't. Ali Smith's writing is richly inventive, thought-provoking and full of dark humour. She takes the aphorism (and Muriel Spark novel) *Memento mori* 'Remember you must die' and turns it on its head — 'Remember you must live'. This is not a novel that deals with events, more with the tiny incidents that happen between events. But despite the apparently random quality of much of the narrative, the novel doesn't meander, it still drives forward. Experimental writing, yes, but never gimmicky and never less than enjoyable.

The story starts some months after the tragedy and Sara's ghost is fading. Words and meanings elude her. Tastes, colours and smells are all disappearing and she longs for contact with the material world, some little irritation of the flesh '... a small sharp stone, so that it jags into different parts of the sole and hurts just enough to be pleasure'. Obsessed with her swimming speeds when alive, even in death she needs to know how fast she fell. The ghost tries to insinuate itself into its broken body rotting under the ground, begging for a story, the story of their death. And the details of Sara's death are awful, but the ghost's playful irreverence is comic – 'Dead leg. Dead arm. Dead hand. Dead eye. Dead I.' It is even smugly pleased that Sara died in a classy hotel. This opening chapter is a poignant reminder of how quickly life passes and how much of it passes us by.

Remember you must live.

From Sara and her sudden death we move to Else (Elspeth) Freeman, the homeless beggar, ill with chronic bronchitis. Everything about Else is reduced and distilled, even her words. From her pitch on the pavement opposite the Global Hotel she asks passers-by if they can 'Spr sm chn?' She has all day to notice the tiny details of her restricted world, to think about words and their meanings. She plays games with her own name, pretending people need her when they say 'I don't know what, Else, to do.' She has been loved. She and her boyfriend, Ade once kissed coins from one to another, 'flat on her tongue like a communion wafer'. Smith dwells on the minutiae of life, making us look again with heightened awareness, offering sudden, vivid descriptions. Starlings' chests are 'punctured with stars'. Copper tastes 'like meat gone off'. Else likes to wrap her feet in newspapers with relevant headlines about social injustice; she visits the library and reads metaphysical poetry because she 'can't be bothered with novels any more ... They take too long. They say too much...' Else's poverty and the unconscious luxury of the Global Hotel are brought into even starker contrast when Lise the receptionist smuggles her into a room for the night. Else's first indulgence once the door is closed is a massive fit of coughing 'one of the best ... she roared and hacked like a lion'. She has a bath but doesn't use the towels because 'they're too white'. Finally, unable to settle, she leaves the Global and goes back to the streets and her evening pastime of looking through people's windows and watching them live their lives.

At first Lise O'Brien appears to be the character most in control of her life. She smuggles Else into a room and later gives Clare, Sara's sister, a free breakfast. With these Robin Hood gestures of defiance she takes revenge on her faceless employers. But we don't know what's around the corner and what's lying in wait for Lise is an illness that makes her incapable of doing anything. Her story starts six months in the future, 'Lise was lying in bed. That was practically all the story there was.' She seems to have some form of chronic fatigue syndrome – a condition also suffered by Ali Smith – and everything exhausts her. She tries to complete a pointless Incapacity for Work Questionnaire but can only recall advertising jingles from her childhood. Words won't work for her anymore. During this section the focus shifts from Lise to her mother Deirdre, a woman whose life has been given a new purpose by her daughter's illness. Looking after Lise has inspired her to write an epic poem called 'Hotel World'. Such rhymes as 'inspire us' for 'virus' and 'perm' for 'germ' tell us all we need to know about Deirdre's writing skills but there's no doubting the depth of her love for her daughter as she gently strokes her hair away from her eyes as she lies sleeping.

Penny Warner is a journalist, staying at the Global to write a piece of advertising copy for her newspaper, *The World*. She is the worst communicator of them all. She misreads situations, misunderstands what people say to her and as soon as she has committed a few words to her laptop, she forgets them. Bored and ready to be distracted she helps Clare Wilby and Else prise a panel off the wall in the corridor outside her room, revealing the dumb waiter lift shaft. She's willing to believe that Clare is a hotel employee and doesn't recognise Else's poverty, instead she sees 'some kind of druggy eccentric guest or maybe even a minor ex-rock star'. When Else walks out of the Global Penny follows, thinking that she is going to look at houses with a view to buying them. When finally the 'penny drops' she still borrows money from Else to phone for a taxi. In a fit of generosity she writes Else a cheque, but cancels it as soon as she gets back to the hotel, 'something inside her which had been forced open had sealed up again'. Penny lives on the surface of life failing to connect with anyone. 'Why not let yourself get utterly oblivious?' she writes in her spectacularly meaningless advertising copy. Which is of course exactly what she does.

By the time we arrive at Clare's story we have already observed her at Sara's funeral 'with a fracture of anger starting under her yellow hairline' and dropping clocks and shoes down the empty lift shaft at the Global. I found Clare Wilby's anger and confusion over her sister's death intensely moving and her stream-of-consciousness inner monologue powerfully depicts her grief. She has to see for herself where her sister died and establish that it wasn't suicide. She speaks to Duncan who was with Sara that night and is absurdly delighted to discover the speed with which Sara fell – so fast it was almost like breaking a swimming record. Clare is proud of her sister and how she almost made it to the subs for the national team. She thinks of all the things Sara could have been and tries to keep her alive by watching TV for her and eating toast slowly to remember it for her. Her grief is desperately poignant but her memories aren't sentimental, she remembers the fights and the arguments as well. She tells Sara, 'Less than 4 seconds that's all you took I know I counted it for you.' It should bring peace to Sara and her ghost.

The novel ends with life and love. Not long before she died Sara fell in love for the very first time; to her surprise it was with a girl in a watch shop, but she was too shy to do anything about it. The girl in the shop is happy and full of anticipation, wearing Sara's watch and waiting for her to return. We know that Sara is dead but somehow that doesn't make the watch girl's newly awakened love any less hopeful. Life really does go on and Sara's ghost has the final word.

Wooooo-
  hooooooo
              oo
                  o

So there you have it. A book about death that's full of energy and life. An innovative, disturbing novel which is at times hilariously funny. A book that makes you open your eyes to the power and the possibilities of language. A story that you will want to read again.

How can you resist?

The extract

Hotel World

Past

Woooooooo-

hooooooo what a fall what a soar what a plummet what a dash into dark into light what a plunge what a glide thud crash what a drop what a rush what a swoop what a fright what a mad hushed skirl what a smash mush mash-up broke and gashed what a heart in my mouth what an end.

What a life.

What a time.

What I felt. Then. Gone.

Here's the story; it starts at the end. It was the height of the summer when I fell; the leaves were on the trees. Now it's the deep of the winter (the leaves fell off long ago) and this is it, my last night, and tonight what I want more than anything in the world is to have a stone in my shoe. To be walking along the pavement here outside the hotel and to feel a stone rattling about in my shoe as I walk, a small sharp stone, so that it jags into different parts of the sole and hurts just enough to be pleasure, like scratching an itch. Imagine an itch. Imagine a foot, and a pavement beneath it, and a stone, and pressing the stone with my whole weight hard into the skin of the sole, or against the bones of the bigger toes, or the smaller toes, or the inside curve of the foot, or the heel, or the small ball of the muscle that keeps a body upright and balanced and moving across the breathtaking still-hard surface of the world.

Because now that my breath, you might say, has been taken I miss such itching detail all the time. I don't want anything but it. I worry endlessly at detail that would never have concerned me, not even for a moment of when I was still alive. For example, just for peace of mind, my fall. I would like very much to know how long it took, how long exactly, and I'd do it again in a minute given the chance, the gift of a chance, the chance of a living minute, sixty whole seconds, so many. I'd do it given only a fraction of that with my full weight behind me again if I could (and this time I'd throw myself willingly down it wooo-

hooooo and this time I'd count as I went, one elephant two eleph-ahh) if I could feel it again, how I hit it, the basement, from four floors up, from toe to head, dead. Dead leg. Dead arm. Dead hand. Dead eye. Dead I, four floors between me and the world, that's all it took to take me, that's the measure of it, the length and death of it, the short goodb—.

Quite tall roomy floors, quite quality floors. Nobody could say I didn't have a classy passage out; the rooms very newly and tastefully furnished with good hard expensive beds and corniced high ceilings on the first and second, and a wide grand stairwell I fell parallel to down the back of. Twenty-one steps between each floor and sixteen down to the basement; I fell them all. Quite substantial space from each thick carpet above to each thick carpet below though the basement is stone (I remember it, hard) and the drop was short, less than one complete glorious second per floor I estimate now so long after the event, descent, end. It was something fine. The fall. The feeling. The one-off rough-up; the flight to the bitter end, all the way down to the biting of dust.

A mouthful of dust would be something. You could gather it any time, couldn't you, any time you like, from the corners of rooms, the underneaths of beds, the tops of doors. The rolled-up hairs and dried stuff and specks of what-once-was-skin, all the glamorous leavings of breathing creatures ground down to essence and glued together with the used-up leftover webs and the flakes of a moth, the see-through flakes of a bluebottle's dismantled wing. You could easily (for you can do such a thing whenever you choose, if you want to) smear your hand with dust, roll dust's precious little between a finger and a thumb and watch it stencil into your fingerprint, yours, unique, nobody else's. And then you could lick it off; I could lick it off with my tongue, if I had a tongue again, if my tongue was wet, and I could taste it for what it is. Beautiful dirt, grey and vintage, the grime left by life, sticking to the bony roof of a mouth and tasting of next to nothing, which is always better than nothing.

I would give anything to taste. To taste just dust.

Because now that I'm nearly gone, I'm more here than I ever was. Now that I'm nothing but air, all I want is to breathe it. Now that I'm silent forever, haha, it's all words words words with me. Now that I can't just reach out and touch, it's all I want, is to.

This is how it ended. I climbed into the, the. The lift for dishes, very small room waiting suspended above a shaft of nothing, I forget the word, it has its own name. Its walls, ceiling and floor were all silver-coloured metal. We were on the top floor, the third; it used to be the servants' quarters two hundred years ago when the house had servants in it, and after that the house was a brothel and up there was where the cheap girls, the more diseased or aging girls, were put to sell their wares, and now that it's a hotel and each room costs money every night the smaller rooms still cost a little less because the ceilings are closer to touching their floors up at the top of the house. I took the dishes out and put them on the carpet. I was careful not to spill anything. It was only my second night. I was being good. I climbed in, to prove I could; I curled like a snail in a shell with my neck and the back of my head crammed in, pressed hard right up against the metal roof, my face between my arms, my chest between my thighs. I made a perfect circle and the room swayed, the cord snapped, the room fell wooo—

hooooo and broke on the ground, I broke too. The ceiling came down, the floor came up to meet me. My back broke, my neck broke, my face broke, my head broke. The cage round my heart broke open and my heart came out. I think it was my heart. It broke out of my chest and it jammed into my mouth. This is how it began. For the first time (too late) I knew how my heart tasted.

I have been missing the having a heart. I miss the noise it used to make, the way it could shift warmth round, the way it could keep me awake. I go from room to room here and see beds wrecked after love and sleep, then beds cleaned and ready, waiting again for bodies to slide into them; crisp sheets folded down, beds with their mouths open saying *welcome, hurry up, get in, sleep is coming.* The beds are so inviting. They open their mouths all over the hotel every night for the bodies which slip into them with each other or alone; all the people with their beating hearts, sliding into spaces left empty for them by other people gone now to God knows where, who warmed the same spaces up only hours before.

I have been trying to remember what it was like, to sleep knowing you would wake up. I have been monitoring them closely, the bodies, and seeing what their hearts let them do. I have been watching them sleep afterwards; I have sat at the ends of satisfied beds, dissatisfied beds, snoring, oblivious, insomniac beds, the beds of people who sensed no one there, no one else in the room but them.

Hurry up. Sleep is coming. The colours are going. I saw that the traffic was colourless today, the whole winter street was faded, left out in the wind and the sun for too long. Today even the sun was colourless, and the sky. I know what this means. I saw the places where green used to be. I saw almost no reds, and no blues at all. I will miss red. I will miss blue and green. I will miss the shapes of women and men. I will miss the smell of my own feet in summer. I will miss the smell. My feet. Summer. Buildings and the way they have windows. The bright packaging round foods. Small coins that are not worth much, the weight of them in the pocket or a hand. I will miss hearing a song or a voice come out of a radio. Seeing fires. Seeing grass. Seeing birds. Their wings. Their beady   . The things they see with. The things we see with, two of them, stuck in a face above a nose. The word's gone. I had it a moment ago. In birds they're black and like beads. In people they're small holes surrounded in colour: blue, green or brown. Sometimes they can be grey, grey is also a colour. I will miss seeing. I will miss my fall that ruined me, that made me wooo -

hooooo what I am today. What a fuck, for always, for ever and ever world-without-end with an end after all, amen. I'd do it again and again. I go every night since I fell last summer (my last) up to the top floor, and though the lift is gone now, to God knows where, removed out of something akin to good taste (notorious, a tragedy, not-spoken-about, a shadow story, my dying got into the papers one day and blew away the next, a hotel has to make a living), the shaft is still there suspended behind the stairwell with its grave promise from up all the way to down, and I throw myself over and it's all I can do, hover in the hollow, settle to the ground like boring snow. Or if I launch myself in, make a special effort to fly down fast to hit the stone, I go straight through it as if the stone is water, or I'm a hot blade and the stone is butter. I can make no dent in anything. I have nothing left to break.

Imagine diving into water, water breaking round your shoulders to make room for you in it. Imagine hot or cold. Imagine cold butter disappearing into heated-up bread, gold on its surface, going. There is a word for heated-up bread. I know it. I knew it. No, it's gone.

Here's the story. When I hit the basement whoo I was broke apart, flaked away off the top of me like the points of flame off the top of a fire. I went to the funeral to see who I'd been. It was a bit gloomy. It was a cold day in June; people had coats on. Actually it is very nice, where they buried her. Birds sing in its trees, and the sound of far-away traffic; I could hear the full range of sounds then. Now the birds are far away, and there is almost no traffic noise. I visit quite often. It's winter now. They've put up a stone with her name and her dates and an oval photograph on it. It hasn't faded yet. It will, in time; it gets the late afternoon sun. Other stones have this too, the same kind of photograph, and the rain gets in and as the seasons move round the stones, heating them up and cooling them down, condensation comes and goes inside the glass over the pictures. That small boy with the school cap on, way across the moundy grass; that elderly lady, beloved wife; that young man in his best suit twenty-five years out of fashion; all still breathing behind their glass. I hope ours will do that breathing thing too. Hers.

Under the ground, in the cold, in the rich small smells of soil and wood and dampening varnish, so many exciting things are happening to her now. Maybe the earnest ticklish mouths of the worms; anything. We were a girl, we died young; the opposite of old, we died it. We had a name and nineteen summers; it says as much on the stone. Hers/mine. She/I. Knock knock. Wooo-

hoooo's there? Me. You wooo-

hoooo? You-hoo yourself. Someone has cut the photograph of her so it will fit in. I can see the tremor of careful scissors round the edge of her head. A girl's head, dark hair to the shoulders. Closed and smiling mouth. Bright and shy, the things she saw with. They once were greenish blue. The head in the glass oval is the same one in the frames in the different rooms of the house, one in the front room, one in the parents' room, one in the hall. I chose the saddest people and I followed them to see where we'd lived. They seemed vaguely familiar. They sat at the front of the church. I couldn't be sure. I had to guess. I thought they were ours, the people, and I was right. After the funeral we went home. The house is small; it has no upstairs, no place for a good fall. A chair in that house can take up almost one whole wall. A couch and two chairs fill a room so there is hardly any place for the legs of the people sitting.

A dog was barking at me two houses away. A cat shivered through me where her ankles had been, rubbing up against air. More funeral people came and the house got even smaller. I watched them take tea in the lack of space she'd lived in. I went to her room. It was full of two beds. I hovered above a bed. I came back through. I hovered above the sad. I hovered above the television. I hovered above the hoover.

They ate the salmon, the salad and the little sandwiches and they left, shaking hands with the man at the door, the father. They were relieved to be leaving. The blackness dispersed above the heads of most of them when they reached the garden gate and clicked it behind them. I went back inside the house to examine the left people. There were three. The woman was the saddest. She sat in a chair and the unspoken words which hung round her head said: although this is my home where I have lived for twenty-two years, and in it I am surrounded by family and familiar things, I do not rightly know any more where it is that I am in the world. The man made tea and cleared dishes. All afternoon while tea was being drunk or was skinning over he collected up cups on a tray and went through to the kitchen, filled a kettle and made more tea, brought cups back again full of it. In the kitchen he stood, opened a cupboard door, took nothing out of the cupboard, shut the door again. The still-alive child was a girl, another one. She had a fracture of anger starting under her yellow hairline, crossing her forehead and running right down the middle of her face, dividing her chin, her neck, her chest, all the way to her abdomen where it snarled itself into a black knot. This knot only just held the two halves of her together. She sat hugging her knees below the framed photograph of the gone girl. In it we were wearing a tie, shy, and holding a trophy in the shape of a swimmimg body.

There was some salmon left on the plate. I was wondering how it would taste. The man came through, took it away, scraped it into a plastic bag in the back yard. It was a waste. He could have kept it. They could have eaten it later or tomorrow and it would have tasted as good, better; I wanted him to know. I looked at him sadly, then shyly, then he saw me. He dropped the plastic bag. It rustled down on to the broken flagstones. His mouth opened. No sound came out (I could still hear perfectly then). I waved my swimming trophy at him. He paled. He smiled. He shook his head and looked through me, and then I was gone again and he threw the salmon away. A whole half a side of a fish, and the bones would have been easy to pick out, it was perfectly cooked. It had beautiful pinkness. This was last summer, my (suddenly) last. I could still see the full range of reds then.

So I practised the school photograph which was on top of the television. The face was innocence and tiredness, the age thirteen, a slight squint in the, the. The things she saw with. I honed to perfection the redness in them in another picture, one with other girls, and all the girls in the blur had red lights and mock boldness coming out of their faces and drinks in their hands. I checked to see I was performing the right girl. There she was, hiding at the back. I worked hard at the warmth of her look in the picture on the mantlepiece, the one with her arm round the shoulders of the woman now sitting so lostly in the chair. Her mother.

I could do the self in the oval on the headstone

without even trying; it was easy, slight smile but serious; passport photograph for entry to other worlds. But my favourite to perform was the one with the left-behind sister in it too, a picture the sister kept hidden in her purse and only looked at after her parents were asleep or when she was in a room with a lock. Both of them sat on a couch, but the gone girl was caught in the middle of saying something, looking away from the camera. That one was my masterpiece, the angle of movement, the laughing look, the still more about to be said. That one took effort, to look so effortless.

From summer to autumn I did all that I can. I appeared to the father. I appeared to the mother. I appeared to the sister. The father pretended he couldn't see. The more he saw, the more he looked away. A wall crept inches higher from his shoulders round his head; every time I came he added a new layer of bricks to the top of it. By autumn the wall was way past the top of his head, swaying, badly bricklayed and dangerously unbalanced, nearly up to the ceiling in the living room where it knocked against the lampshade and sent light and shadow spinning every time he crossed the room.

I came only twice to the mother. It made her cry, made her miserable, jumpy and fearful. It was unpleasant. Both times ended in tears and sleepless weeks. It was kinder not to do it, and so I left her alone.

But the sister drained me with a terrible thirst. I couldn't appear enough for her. With the trophy, with the red lights coming out of my face, with the passport smile, with the laughing things unsaid. Every face I made drained and disappeared into the fracture that ran the length of her body. Summer passed, autumn came and she was still dark with thirst; if anything she was thirstier, she wanted more, and the colours were fading. When winter came I stopped. (It has been easier since then, I find, to appear to people who don't recognize what they see. I looked at the cracked face of the sad girl and knew. In the face of so much meaning it is easier to have no face.)

Above me the birds singing, further and further away. Each day a little further, more muffled, like wool in the ears. (Imagine wool. The rough-thready rub of it) I sat an inch above the grave on cushy air. It was Saturday afternoon; I was bored with upsetting the family, bored with appearing to random people who didn't know who we were. The leaves were paling on the trees. The grass, neat and new, was greying for winter, and her underneath the sodden carpet, soil piled and turned for four luxurious feet above her. I looked at the passport in the oval, the face of the shape we had taken together. Down through the soil she slept. She couldn't come up. But I could go down. Down through loam and the laid eggs of many-legged creatures, and the termites, the burrowing feasty maggots, all waiting for it to break them open, the season after winter, I forget the word for it, the season when the flowers will push their heads regardless out again.

Down I went far further than stupefied bulbs till I passed through the lid of the wooden room, smooth and costly on the outside, chipboard-cheap at the centre.

One last time I slipped into our old shape, hoisting her shoulders round me and pushing down into her legs and arms and through her splintery ribs, but the fitting was ill, she was broken and rotting, so I lay half-in, half-out of her under the ruched frills of the room's innards, cold I reckon, and useless pink in the dark.

The things she saw with had blackened. Her mouth was glued shut. Hello, she said through the glue. You again. What are you after?

How are you? I said. Sleep well?

(She heard me!) Fine till now, she said. Well? What? This had better be good.

I just want something, I whispered, to take to the surface. Just the one something. It's Saturday. Did you know? Your sister planted crocuses above your head last week, did you know?

Who? she said. What? Fuck off. Leave me alone. I'm dead, for God's sake.

I need to know something, I said. Can you remember the fall? Can you remember how long it took us? Can you remember what happened before it? Please.

Silence. (But I knew she could hear me.)

I won't leave, I said, until you tell me. I won't go till I get it.

Silence. So I waited. I lay there for days in the box room with her. I irritated her as a matter of course. I played with her stitches. I slipped in and out of her. I went in one ear and out the other, I sang songs from West End musicals (oh what a beautiful morning; all I want is a room somewhere / far away from the cold night air;

cheerio but be back soon; sue me, sue me / shoot bullets through me / I love you), I sang them into the back of her skull till complaints rolling around from the neighbouring graves made me stop. Then I stuck her fingers up her plugged nose instead, tweaked her earlobes.

I missed three whole rise and falls of the sun (precious enough days to me if not her, lying now with her pockets full of soil and a dusting of soil over her so snug and safe in her shaft of days and nights that go on and on and on end-stopped by no base basement) before at last she said unblinkingly:

All right, all right. I'll tell you. If you promise to go away and leave me in peace.

Okay, I will, it's a deal, I said.

You swear? She said.

On your mother's life, I said.

Oh Christ. My mother. Ground number one rule. No reminding me, she said. And number two. Only the fall; no more, nothing else.

Okay, I said. That's all I want.

How much do you know? she said through teeth clamped tight. How far back do I have to go?

Well, I know about taking the dishes out of the little room, I said. I know about being careful. I remember curling into the room, tucking our legs in like someone not yet born, but I can't remember why. And I remember the fall, wooo-

hooooo you bet I do.

I kicked our legs against the thin-wood walls. I could feel she disapproved. With the sigh of one dead she said:

It wasn't a room. It was too small for a room. It was a dumb waiter, remember? –

(That's the name, the name for it; *that's* it; dumb waiter dumb waiter dumb waiter.)

– and here's the story, since you're so desperate for one. Happy is what you realize you are a fraction of a second before it's too late.

about the **author**

Ali Smith

Ali Smith was born in Inverness in 1962. She studied for her first two degrees in Aberdeen before moving to Cambridge to do a PhD in American and Irish modernism. She then returned to Scotland, to Edinburgh, and worked in Glasgow as a university lecturer, a job which she lasted only two years at before she left, disgruntled at and demoralised by academia. After a bout of illness and convalescence (during which she wrote her first collection of stories) and a move back to Cambridge, Ali won the Macallan/*Scotland on Sunday* short story competition and the Saltire First Book Award for *Free Love* in 1995. Her first novel, *Like*, was published in 1997 and a further collection of short stories, *Other Stories And Other Stories*, in 1999. The novel *Hotel World* was nominated for both The Orange Prize for Fiction 2001 and The Booker Prize, and it won the inaugural Scottish Arts Council Book of the Year Award (2002), the Encore Award (2002) and the East England Arts Award (2002). Her most recent work is a

new collection, *The Whole Story and Other Stories*. Ali
Smith also writes for the *Scotsman*, the *TLS* and the
Guardian.

> '*I dislike making pronouncements on writing, as if a
> writer knew the answers to its questions. I don't; that's
> why I write. It's really about questioning,
> communication, a dialogue between the book and the
> reader, the story and the reader, not the writer and the
> reader. It's a thousand times better to read a book or a
> story than to read anything its writer ever says about it.*'
> – Ali Smith, on writing

titles **by**

Ali Smith

Short stories
Free Love
Othe stories and other stories
The Whole Story and other stories

Novels
Like
Hotel World

discussion **points**

1. Five disparate voices inhabit *Hotel World*. Are they all equally strong? Which character do you find most convincing and why?

2. Else, the homeless woman, '... can't be bothered with novels any more... They take too long. They say too much ...'
   And Sara Wilby's corpse is impatient with her ghost's desire for her story, '– and here's the story since you're so desperate for one.'
   In what ways does Ali Smith's narrative structure differ from the conventional story-telling norm?

3. How does Ali Smith inject so much hope and humour into a novel whose subject matter essentially is death?

4. How important is the hotel setting of *Hotel World* and in what ways is the metaphor of the hotel as a corporate 'global' body worked through the novel?

5. There is only one significant male character in *Hotel*

World and he has withdrawn into a cupboard. Is the novel's viewpoint exclusively female? Does this novel appeal more to women than men? (The jacket is very pink!)

6. Ali Smith has said that she is interested in how popular culture affects the meaning and usage of language. Can you find examples of this in *Hotel World?*

press quotes

'Ali Smith has got style, ideas, and punch. Read her.'
– Jeanette Winterson

'*Hotel World* is everything a novel should be: disturbing, comforting, funny, challenging, sad, rude, and beautiful. It can turn from tragedy to hilarity within a sentence, or even a clause. Everyone should check in at their earliest convenience.'
– *Independent on Sunday*

'Emotionally charged and compassionate, Ali Smith's second novel bristles with inventiveness. Remember you must live. And remember that you must read this book.'
– *Scotsman*

'By turns moving, funny, and compassionate, *Hotel World* is, quite simply, the kind of book that will make even the most established writers feel inadequate.'
– *The List*

'Ali Smith has a rare ability to show the profound in the mundane. She is an extremely readable, easy-flowing

writer, and one of the subtlest and most intelligent around.'
— *Independent*

'Smith has pulled off an ambitious, disturbing, and immensely affecting experiment and made it work brilliantly.'
— *Big Issue*

'A greatly appealing read and a remarkable novel.'
— *Washington Post*

similar **reads**

Other Stories and Other Stories by Ali Smith
(Granta; ISBN: 1862071861)
Smith's precise use of language and her eye for the unusual in the everyday are to the fore in this haunting collection of short stories published in 1999.

Way to Go by Alan Spence
(Phoenix; ISBN: 0753807327)
A young man reluctantly inherits his father's funeral business, but he's determined to do things differently. There must be a better 'way to go'. A seriously funny book about the Scottish way of death and the inadequacy of our mourning rituals.

O Caledonia by Elspeth Barker
(Penguin; ISBN: 0140154728)
Another great beginning, another bizarre teenage death. Set in Scotland in the 1940s and '50s, this beautifully written novel sets out the chain of events leading to sixteen-year-old Janet's untimely end. A superb blend of tragedy and pitch-black comedy.

The Hundred and Ninety-Nine Steps
by Michel Faber

(Canongate; ISBN: 1841953288)

Siân suffers a recurring dream about her own horrific death and in an effort to block out the nightmares joins an archaeological dig at Whitby Abbey. Faber unearths the ways in which the past haunts the present in a novella that is part ghost story, part thriller and part old-fashioned romance.

Ascension Day by Chris Dolan

(Review; ISBN: 0747275459)

In his imaginative and poetic first novel, Chris Dolan charts the unlikely connections between a group of neighbours whose lives suddenly collide one afternoon when three of them ascend into Glasgow's cloudy skies.

Stopping for Death: Poems of Death and Loss
edited by Carol Ann Duffy

(Viking; ISBN: 0670854166)

Personal and public bereavement is explored across time, place, race and religion in a wonderful selection of poems chosen to comfort, amuse and even provoke. Interesting that this was published as an anthology for young people.

competition

Your chance to win ten contemporary works of fiction signed by their authors.

The *Read Around Books* series was developed by Scottish Book Trust to encourage readers to widen their reading interests and discover writers they had never tried before. Has it been a success? We want to hear from you. Tell us if you have enjoyed this little series or not and if you did, do you have any suggestions for authors who should be included in the series in the future.

Writer to us now with the following information:

Name and address
Email address
Are you a member of a readers' group?
Name of reader's group

Send us the information above and we will enter you into our prize draw to be drawn on 22 August 2003.

Send to:
RAB Draw
Scottish Book Trust
137 Dundee Street
Edinburgh EH11 1BG

scottish **book trust**

What is Scottish Book Trust?

Scottish Book Trust exists to serve readers and writers in Scotland. We work to ensure that everyone has access to good books, and to related resources and opportunities.

We do this in a number of ways:

- By operating the Writers in Scotland Scheme, which funds over 1,400 visits a year by Scottish writers to a variety of institutions and groups
- By supporting Scottish writing through a programme of professional training opportunities for writers
- By publishing a wide variety of resources and leaflets to support readership
- By promoting initiatives such as National Poetry Day and World Book Day
- And through our Book Information Service, providing free advice and support to readers and writers, and the general public.

For more information please visit
<u>www.scottishbooktrust.com</u>

titles **in the series**

Available in the Read Around Books series

Iain Crichton Smith's *Murdo: The Life and Works,*
   by Douglas Gifford

Meaghan Delahunt's *In The Blue House,*
   by Gavin Wallace

Michel Faber's *Under the Skin,* by Mary Firth

Jonathan Falla's *Blue Poppies,* by Rosemary Goring

Janice Galloway's *Clara,* by David Robinson

Andrew Greig's *That Summer,* by Alan Taylor

Anne MacLeod's *The Dark Ship*, by Lindsey Fraser

Maggie O'Farrell's *After You'd Gone,* by Rosemary Goring

Suhayl Saadi's *The Burning Mirror,*
   by Catherine McInerney

Ali Smith's *Hotel World,* by Kathryn Ross

Muriel Spark's *The Comforters,* by Alan Taylor

Alexander Trocchi's *Young Adam,* by Gillian Mackay